PREDATOR
CONTROL

PREDATOR CONTROL

Prepared by
the Advisory Service of Game Conservancy Ltd

THE GAME CONSERVANCY
Fordingbridge
Hampshire SP6 1EF
Telephone No : 0425 652381

ISBN 0 9500130 6 4

All photographs, unless otherwise stated, by Game Conservancy Ltd

Front Cover: Mink with fish (Aquila Photographics)

Printed and bound in Great Britain by
BAS Printers Limited, Over Wallop, Hampshire

Published by
Game Conservancy Ltd
Fordingbridge, Hampshire SP6 1EF

CONTENTS

Acknowledgement: The Game Conservancy acknowledges the
kind assistance of Kenny Wilson, John Walsha, Charlie Parkes and
John Thornley in compiling this guide.

SECTION A. INTRODUCTION

CHAPTER ONE

Controlling Predation – the Basic Aim

The fundamental aim of any shoot is to produce enough game to allow some to be harvested. Since the game itself, of whichever species, is a prey of other animals, it follows that control of predation is an important part of the game conservation package. At the same time it is important to recognise that success <u>may not</u> be directly related to how many predators are killed. In the final analysis it is the response of the game population to control which counts. The aim of this guide is to show how to control predation in a way which maximises game survival, while still recognising the conservation needs of the predator species.

Carefully targeted predation control is essential for good gamebird production. (Photo: T H Blank)

The Victorian Legacy

Predator control has been at the very heart of game management in Britain ever since game shooting for sport was seriously developed in the mid 19th Century. Indeed on these Victorian shoots predator control or 'vermin destruction' was the principal activity of an army of gamekeepers who, in many areas, occupied contiguous series of beats from one end of the country to the other. Labour was cheap and nobody particularly cared about the well-being of birds of prey and predatory mammals. Thus, by Edwardian times game populations were at a record level. Partly as a result of this persecution some populations of raptor and carnivore had been virtually wiped off the map.

It is therefore little wonder that since the Second World War, when interest in conservation was brought about by industrial pollution, pesticides and the destruction of countryside features such as hedgerows, predator control has often been regarded as fundamentally counter to conservation. *The Game Conservancy Trust believes such a view is wholly mistaken and that, if carried out carefully and selectively, predator control will help to produce a surplus of wild game to shoot. This in turn helps to justify the retention of hedgerows and game coverts, so on balance predator control actually makes a positive contribution to wildlife conservation in general.*

Landowners and game keepers must understand the rationale behind their predator control programmes, not only so they can make it work effectively to produce wild game, but also so they can justify it to other countryside users who may not understand why it is necessary. At all times we must remember that the aim is to reduce the level of *predation on game*, not just to kill the largest number of predators.

The Scientific Rationale

A common concept is that predators only take the sick and weak from prey populations, and the presence of a few predators has a positive influence in weeding out unhealthy individuals. To an extent this is true, particularly where predators have to pursue their prey, and scenes on television of lions or cheetahs chasing a victim from large herds of ungulates clearly demonstrate how they seek out animals that are slightly less strong than others. However, it is a fallacy that predators *only* take sick and weak individuals; in many cases the victims are fully mature breeding animals which happen to have been caught in the wrong place at the wrong time. In any case, in most predator/prey systems there would simply not be enough sick or weakly animals to support the whole predator complex.

Somewhat allied to this is the view that predators only take animals that will eventually die anyway, and therefore are for the most part considered to be a 'doomed surplus'. In red grouse, for example, territorial behaviour of adult cocks may lead to some individuals not obtaining a territory and many of these excluded individuals will subsequently die. In fact, what a game manager is trying to do is to produce an 'optimum sustainable yield'. This is the biggest possible harvest without causing any long-term deterioration in habitat or game. Usually the breeding stock required for 'optimum sustainable yield' is lower than the maximum possible. There is no such thing as a 'doomed surplus' in such a situation.

Analysis of the diet of various predators is often used to assess their relative importance. These analyses are normally presented as different prey items expressed as a percentage of the total food intake. Where gamebirds or their eggs figure infrequently, it is quite often argued that the predators are unimportant to game. However, this is not a logical conclusion from the data – it simply demonstrates that *game* is unimportant to the *predator* ; the reverse – that predators are unimportant for game – does not follow. For example, 60% of a stoat's diet may consist of rabbits and only 15% of partridges or pheasants, but if game density is low and stoats are plentiful this could be enough to remove almost the entire partridge and pheasant population. On the other hand, rabbits may be so numerous that the stoat's consumption of them has no measurable effect on the number of rabbits.

The stomach contents of a fox. With such a varied diet, foxes can be sustained at a very high density and cause significant damage to gamebirds, even though they are not an important food for them.

The Need for a System

There has been much discussion among scientists about the effectiveness of keepers in controlling predator numbers at all. Certainly, in many cases, a small scale effort or a casual attempt at predator control is largely a waste of time – the odd fox killed will quickly be replaced by another looking for a suitable vacant territory. If any predator control programme is to be attempted, it should be done in a systematic and determined way.

On most lowland shoots predation is only a major problem during the nesting season. So a deliberate effort should be made to remove the key predators just before nesting and keep them at bay until after the game has hatched (Figure 1). After this the programme may be relaxed, perhaps confining control to selected areas around pheasant release pens.

In upland areas on grouse moors, winter predation by foxes can also be a problem, so for this habitat the campaign must be an extended winter and spring programme. These seasonal programmes usually mean that the keeper has to remove the resident predators every year. Over the years he will probably be killing approximately the same number annually, but this does not mean that he is simply skimming off the surplus each year and having no effect, as many people have argued. What is happening is that he is providing temporary relief from predation at the most critical time and thus ensuring a much enhanced chance of successful game breeding.

In spite of the above, many people continue to argue that the benefits of predator control are likely to be small relative to other aspects of game management such as habitat improvement or reduction in pesticide use. In 1984 The Game Conservancy Trust began an experiment designed to show the significance of predation to partridge production.

Two similar areas of countryside on Salisbury Plain were taken as study areas. In 1984 these had similar partridge numbers in September (230 & 223). Employing a gamekeeper on one, this autumn number increased to 318 birds in 1987, whereas without predator control the stock on the other area declined to only 79

5

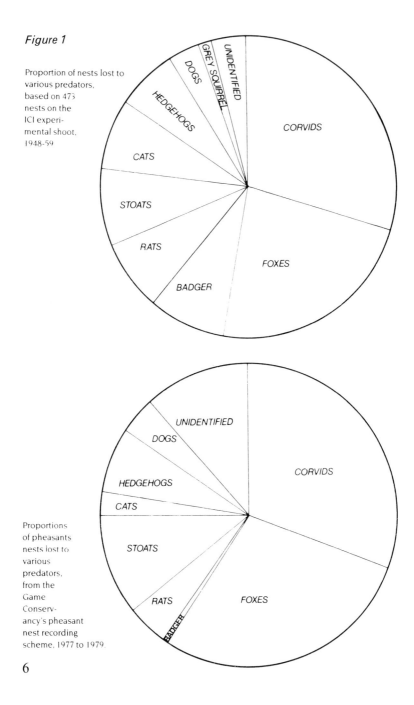

Figure 1

Proportion of nests lost to various predators, based on 473 nests on the ICI experimental shoot, 1948-59

CORVIDS

GREY SQUIRREL

UNIDENTIFIED

DOGS

HEDGEHOGS

CATS

STOATS

RATS

BADGER

FOXES

UNIDENTIFIED

DOGS

HEDGEHOGS

CATS

STOATS

RATS

BADGER

FOXES

CORVIDS

Proportions of pheasants nests lost to various predators, from the Game Conservancy's pheasant nest recording scheme, 1977 to 1979.

6

birds. In 1988 the treatments were switched, resulting in a recovery of the unkeepered population to 383 by the autumn of 1990. Meanwhile the previously keepered population fell to 117 when left to itself. Furthermore over six years the keepered beats yielded a bag of 437 wild grey partridge, whereas on the areas left natural only 121 were bagged.

This study is just one of an increasing body of evidence which shows the importance of predation on game.

CHAPTER TWO

An Outline of The Law

Before tackling any form of predator control it is essential to have a clear knowledge of the legislation that protects much of our wildlife. The laws are quite complex and the unenlightened could easily find themselves in a court of law if they ruthlessly set out to destroy all that they consider vermin from the point of view of game. This chapter deals only with UK law: the overseas reader will need to check local laws before using methods described in this book.

There are several Acts of Parliament which are relevant to predator control; the main one is the Wildlife and Countryside Act, which in 1981 replaced the earlier Bird Protection Acts. Certain grey areas of this Act still need to be tested in the courts, but the Wildlife and Countryside Act defines specifically the animals which may be killed, in what circumstances, and what methods may be used. Broadly speaking the Act works on the premises that *mammals* are unprotected except for certain species while all *birds* have protection unless they are listed as exceptions.

Birds

Within the framework of bird protection, certain groups are treated differently according to their listing in the Schedules of the Act.

Among predatory birds which are protected by special penalties, the gamekeeper should note that the following species, among others, are included in Schedule 1:

Barn owl
Snowy owl
Golden eagle
Goshawk
Gyr falcon

Harriers (all species)
Hobby
Honey buzzard
Merlin
Osprey
Peregrine falcon
Red kite

These birds are given full protection, even from disturbance whilst nesting. Breaking this law will result in special penalties, with fines up to £2000. Under *no circumstances* should a keeper kill or a landowner allow his keeper to kill any of the birds listed in Schedule 1. Many are rare and vulnerable species. The employer can be found guilty for causing or permitting the offence as well as his keeper for committing it.

Other birds of prey, including the common buzzard, the kestrel, the sparrowhawk, the little owl and the tawny owl have general protection, for which the maximum penalty is £2000. One may only take such species if one is prepared to show in a court of law that the action was necessary to prevent *serious* damage to 'livestock' or fisheries, and that all other measures had failed. Partridges and pheasants are normally regarded as 'livestock' only if they are completely contained in a pen.

The Wildlife and Countryside Act also has provision for licensing or control of otherwise protected species. This can be in the form of specific licences, issued by the Agriculture and Environment Departments, for individuals to take specified numbers of birds for given reasons, and also 'open general licences' for Authorised Persons (ie all landowners and their employees and people with their permission) to take birds. There are open licences giving a list of birds which may be killed by an authorised person at any time. These species are mostly pests and are:

Collared dove
Carrion and hooded crow
Feral pigeon
Greater black-backed gull
Herring gull

All birds of prey are protected by law. (Photo: Raymond Chaplin)

House sparrow
Jackdaw
Jay
Lesser black-backed gull
Magpie
Rook
Starling
Wood pigeon.

All these species may be legitimate targets for the gamekeeper, but he is not allowed to kill in any way he chooses. Specifically forbidden are snares, spring traps, *poisons of all types including stupefying baits*, bird limes, shooting at night with a lamp and shooting from a motor vehicle. He may however use a smallbore rifle or shotgun. Semi-automatic weapons capable of firing more than three shots are prohibited except for crop protection and in any case would require a firearm certificate. He may also use a cage trap. If the landowner or farmer has a particular pest problem with one of these species and is unable to control them with conventional methods, the Ministry of Agriculture Fisheries and Food (MAFF) is allowed to authorise the use of poisons under controlled conditions, provided it is supervised by their own officials.

It should be noted that moorhens and coots, which may sometimes cause damage to game and waterfowl, may only be taken during the season between September 1 and January 31.

Mammals

The protection of mammals by law is relatively new, and the Wildlife and Countryside Act (1981) replaces the Conservation of Wild Creatures and Wild Plants Act, 1975. There are two categories of mammalian protection. First, Schedule 5 lists *fully* protected species which include the otter, the wild cat, the pine marten and the red squirrel. Their protection includes provisions against disturbance and destruction of shelter. The second category (Schedule 6) includes the following species: hedgehog, polecat, badger. These are

11

When foxes take up residence in badger setts, keepers must apply to MAFF for a licence before they take any action. (Photo: Raymond Chaplin)

protected only from certain *methods* of control. Illegal methods include all traps, all forms of snare, any poison or gas. Night shooting equipment, such as lamps, is prohibited for these species, as are fully automatic weapons. With the notable exception of the badger (which is covered by the Badgers Act) a keeper may kill any of these Schedule 6 species provided he does not use one of the prohibited methods. If he is faced with a problem of, say, a polecat troubling his released pheasants, he could legally use a shotgun to remove it.

The Wildlife and Countryside Act incorporates further restrictions on the use of snares. The 'self-locking' snare is totally banned and all snares must be checked daily.

12

The Badgers Act 1992 essentially prohibits landowners from taking any action against badgers directly. They can now do so only under the auspices of MAFF. There is a growing problem of foxes using badger setts as the numbers of both species increase. Keepers wishing to deal with foxes which have taken up residence in badger setts must apply to MAFF for a licence to use terriers to control the foxes.

There are various other Acts of Parliament which restrict the methods of control of mammals, specifically relating to trapping, poisoning and gassing.

Trapping is mainly restricted by the Pests Act 1954, which makes the gin trap illegal and only allows the use of Ministry approved spring traps to kill mammals. These traps may only be used in an approved manner. The traps permitted at present are:

For rabbits (Traps may only be used "underground in their burrows")	Fenn Mark I Juby Imbra Fenn Rabbit Fenn Mark VI Springer 6
For small mammalian predators including grey squirrels (Traps may only be used in natural and artificial tunnels)	Sawyer Imbra Lloyd Fenn Mark III Juby Fenn Mark IV Fenn Mark VI Springer 4 Springer 6 Kania Trap 2000
For squirrels only	Fuller Garden Trap

While all of these traps may still legally be used, only the Fenn Mark IV, Mark VI, the Springer 4 and 6 and the Kania are in production. The use of catch-alive cage traps is not restricted.

Three Acts of Parliament – the Agriculture Act 1947, the Agriculture Act (Scotland) 1948 and The Food and Environment Protection Act 1985 – restrict the use of poison gas to animals living in holes. Rabbits, moles and rats are, for practical purposes, the only species that can be gassed.

Poisoning mammals is generally illegal except in three circumstances:

1. Against 'small ground vermin' – here one should think in terms of rats and mice only – but see paragraph 3 below.
2. Against moles – strychnine may be used under MAFF permit only.
3. Against grey squirrels – here only Warfarin may be used and then only in areas where there are no red squirrels (see page 75).

   The relevant Acts of Parliament relating to the use of poison are: the Protection of Mammals Act, 1911; the Protection of Animals (Scotland) Act, 1912; Animals (Cruel Poisons) Act, 1962; Agriculture (Miscellaneous Provisions) Act, 1972; The Food and Environment Protection Act, 1985 and the Control of Pesticides Regulation, 1986.

   We must emphasise that although the legal information in this chapter is believed to be correct at the time of going to press, readers should, if in any doubt, check the Acts themselves. As always, the onus is on the individual to make himself aware of the law relating to his actions.

SECTION B.   AVIAN PREDATORS

Introduction

With the exception of the starling, which damages game coverts, all the birds in this section are potential egg thieves, although some are more important than others. While gulls, and even moorhens and coots, are a problem on some shoots, everyone has to contend with members of the crow family – the corvids. Magpies, crows, rooks, jackdaws and jays all take eggs, nestlings and chicks as part of their diet. They also share certain common behavioural traits, which means that control measures are best discussed for the group as a whole, with individual differences raised under species headings.

CHAPTER THREE

Controlling Corvids with Larsen Traps

Corvids are extremely intelligent, and therefore very wary birds. Even when raiding the bird tables of suburban gardens they are much less likely to be taken by surprise than other birds. So the rural corvids are suspicious of people with guns. While shooting will always play its part in corvid control, the results for the effort put in are usually low, and especially so during the nesting season when damage is at its greatest. For this reason, the various cage trapping techniques which The Game Conservancy Trust has pioneered will be the main form of control on most shoots.

Of the five corvid species, the crow (both hooded and carrion) and the magpie are far and away the most serious predators of game. These two species of bird become highly territorial in the spring, defending a comparatively large piece of country against other

Territorial crows and magpies are specialist egg feeders.

members of their own species. Crows will also chase magpies away at this time. During the territorial phase, both species become specialist nest robbers, with eggs, nestlings and chicks forming an important part of their diet. As well as patrolling their territory, they spend considerable amounts of time on look-out duty, watching for intruders and observing the movements of other birds. It appears to be by this method in particular that they spot breeding gamebirds and locate their nests. *The great majority of gamebird nest predation is done by territorial pairs of crows and magpies.*

During the remainder of the year this territorial behaviour breaks down, and crows and magpies take to living more communally, like

16

rooks and jackdaws. This is particularly so with crows, which can form into winter flocks hundreds of birds strong.

The Larsen Trap

The Larsen trap is a cage specifically designed to catch territorial corvids alive and unharmed, using a captive bird of the same species as a lure. It therefore applies especially to crows and magpies, although jays are also territorial and can be caught in the same way. The original Larsen trap was invented by a Danish gamekeeper in the 1950s. It is approximately 80cm square by 40cm high and divided into three compartments. Half of the trap is in the form of a decoy compartment to contain a live corvid, and the other half is divided into two catching compartments with spring-loaded trap doors (Figure 2). Detailed plans of the trap, based closely on the original Danish design, are available from the Sales Centre at Game Conservancy Ltd.

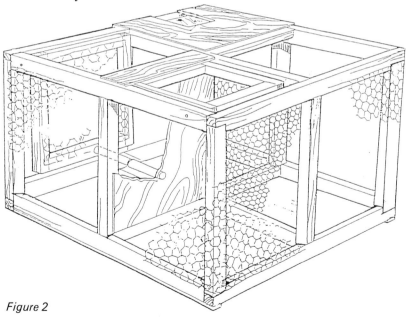

Figure 2

The Larsen Trapping Principle

The urge to evict intruders is so strong in territorial corvids that they usually come very quickly to a Larsen trap with its live decoy. In attempting to chase this bird away they eventually drop into one of the catching compartments and get caught. The second catching compartment is then available to trap the other half of the pair. Sometimes the second bird is much more reluctant to go in. This, however, is not a serious worry, since a single bird is unable to defend its territory and must therefore either find a new mate, or be driven away by another pair. In either case the preoccupations of setting up a new territory prevent the birds from hunting for game nests for some time.

Once they are fully established it is time to bring the Larsen trap back with a new decoy and start the whole procedure again. In this way it is possible to remove new pairs of corvids soon after they arrive and before they start to nest. Provided that the first pairs are removed in early spring, before they have hatched their first broods, there will be no young corvids to starve in their nests, since established pairs do not move into vacated territories and desert their own broods. New pairs are formed from the surplus of otherwise non-breeding birds which have not managed to obtain a territory.

Decoy Welfare

Live decoys must be provided for in a proper manner. As well as being a legal obligation, this also enhances catch rates, since a strong and vigorous caller is much more effective than a weak one. The decoy compartment should be at least partially covered by a solid roof to provide shelter from strong sun or rain. In The Game Conservancy design, half of the roof area is in the form of plywood with a sliding door. If your trap does not have this, a slate or piece of turf is a suitable alternative. A perch beneath this roof is essential too, while if a second one is provided the bird will usually hop from one to the other, and probably catch the eye of target birds in the process.

The bird should be provided with fresh food and water at all times. Water bottles which are strapped to the side of the trap, with a hole in the side, help to keep the water clear for longer than open bowls. Most keepers will provide rabbits as the most convenient food source. Remember to split these open, particularly for magpies which do not have a particularly strong bill. The food should be replaced daily in summer, and old remains removed to keep the cage reasonably clean. An alternative food which is very convenient is canned pet food, or even pre-soaked complete diet. This has the advantage of appearing a little less gory to any passers-by who happen across your trap, which is probably good for public relations. A little piece of food in the catching compartments is a good idea, not as bait but to provide for captives until you check the trap.

Larsen Trapping Techniques

Since the Larsen trap works on the principle of territorial intrusion, there is little point in using a bird as a decoy in the area where it was caught. Thus, as a general principle, each time you catch with your trap, you should move it to a new site. Most people humanely destroy the original decoy bird (with a sharp rap on the head, or using despatch pliers) and use the new captive in a fresh site. It is certainly the case that newly-caught birds are more active, and this probably makes them better as decoys.

Most corvids settle quite quickly in captivity if they are well looked after, and some people therefore feel that it is best to keep a 'tame' bird as a decoy for the entire season. In either case the key to success with this trap is to keep it moving. If you have not caught in a specific place after a couple of days, move to a fresh site. Even a few yards may be all that is needed for success.

While setting the trap in the open is the usual method, trapping in cover helps to reduce the level of vandalism by those who do not understand the need for corvid control. Many people are loath to do this since they feel that the decoy must be highly visible to work. In practice, however, a trap hidden in a bush inside a wood often works well. When a corvid calls in the wood the decoy usually replies and attracts attention to itself.

In open countryside, such as grouse moors and high downland, crows in particular are often difficult to trap. It seems that although they are attracted to the decoy and dance around outside, they are reluctant to jump onto the trap. There are several possible solutions. One is to try one of the many versions of the Larsen with side entry doors. Another is to drive a fence post into the ground inside the trap to give a higher perch. Many keepers have found it helpful to raise the trap onto a bale of straw or something similar. It seems that having a territorial intruder answering you back from above is too much for a crow to bear, so it overcomes its suspicion and jumps up onto the trap to drive the point home. Unfortunately, raising the trap in this way does increase the risk of vandalism. Use of even small patches of cover to conceal the trap can help here,

The Long Meadow trap is one of the most popular side entry Larsens.

and also serve to reduce the 'reluctant crow' syndrome. This is especially applicable to grouse moors if there are odd patches of cover. Many keepers have found that siting their Larsen traps near clumps of rhododendron or pine trees is effective. This is particularly so if the trap is partly concealed in long heather, rushes or dead bracken.

Catching a First Decoy

Obtaining a first decoy to start the Larsen trapping programme is difficult. Both crows and magpies are very suspicious of strange objects like traps, and very unlikely to come to one for bait. The easiest solution to the problem is to beg or borrow a decoy from another keeper (but do not buy, it is illegal to trade in live corvids). If you cannot do this, and are unable to keep a few birds in an aviary from one season to the next, you will have to try with a baited trap.

Probably the best system is to find a favourite corvid perch with a bush or two underneath it. Hide your trap within this bush, with just one catching compartment visible and bait this with an artificial nest with a few eggs in it. It also helps to crack an egg and pour it onto the roof of the trap where it glisters in the sun, and scatter the shells nearby. The overall impression to give is of a part-predated nest which must be emptied as a matter of urgency before the previous raider returns.

Checking Traps

All traps must be checked daily, and Larsens are no exception. In this case, however, it is best to go late in the day so that captives are not kept in the small catching compartment, perhaps without food, overnight. Two or more checks each day are better still. If you find that you have caught one bird, leave the trap for the rest of the day in case its mate comes to join it.

A baited Larsen under a dead tree is one of the most likely ways to catch a first decoy. Most of the trap should be concealed in a bush for best results.

Trapping Seasons

The Larsen system is most effective during the corvids' territorial season, which coincides with the game nesting season. At other times of the year, with no eggs or chicks at risk, there is little point in the gamekeeper wasting effort on catching corvids which are doing no harm.

CHAPTER FOUR

Controlling Corvids with Multi-Catch Cages

Multi-catch cages

While territorial pairs are usually the most serious nest predators, flock-living corvids can also do serious damage. In many cases the sheer weight of numbers means that they come across nests, even if by accident, at far too great a rate. This applies especially if you have large numbers of juvenile crows living nearby, perhaps obtaining their main living on a rubbish tip or outdoor pig unit.

Similar problems apply with moorland situations. Here, if there are no trees, crows will breed on the edges of the moor, defending their territories here, but foraging out onto the moor for grouse nests and other foods. Similar problems can occur with rooks and jackdaws. Wherever possible it pays to get permission from neighbours to trap the boundaries in these situations.

In most such cases Larsen traps are of limited use on the moor itself. Even if the corvids are naive enough to go in and join the decoy when attracted only by the need for company, the rate of catch at one or two birds at a time is too slow to be really effective. On the other hand, the urge to join a feeding flock is great. So a larger cage, with several decoys already in it, is likely to work well. This applies especially in the late winter period, when many keepers like to make a start on their crow control.

The exact design of these multi-catch cages is much less critical than with Larsens. However, three basic types have come to the fore. The roof funnel type, the ground funnel type and the ladder letterbox. In all cases they should be covered with 35mm wire mesh, since smaller sizes trap songbirds.

Roof funnel cages are particularly effective against hoodie crows.

Roof Funnels

This type of trap is particularly popular on the hill for carrion and hoodie crows. It can be made in sections, or permanently sited in places which are known to prove successful from year to year. The trap itself is usually about 3m square and 1.8m high, with a door in one side for access. It has a single roof-funnel entrance which is 120cm square at the top, and framed with wood. This tapers to a round hole at the bottom, 60cm in diameter, and only about 22cm from the ground (Figure 3). The idea is that the crow folds its wings to drop <u>unrestricted</u> down the funnel, but that if it spreads its wings to fly out again it does not have room even if standing exactly in the centre of the circle. Hence the height and diameter of the bottom of the funnel are more critical than the size at the top.

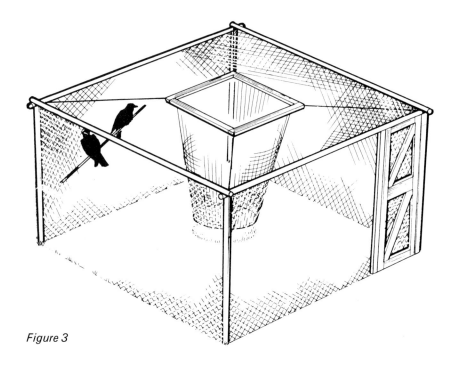

Figure 3

Building such traps around a dead sapling or placing a perch which rises above the trap and leads a bird part way down the funnel are popular schemes which seem to help. The trap is normally baited (with rabbits or other carrion) and left to work during the breeding season, but remains unset, with the door open, at other times. The addition of a couple of live decoys (with food and water) can enhance catches significantly, but they should have some form of shelter. In the uplands it is usually essential to stock-fence cages to prevent damage.

Ground Level Funnels

This type of trap is usually made in sectional form for use on low-ground. The standard, but not critical, size is a 1.8m cube. A ground

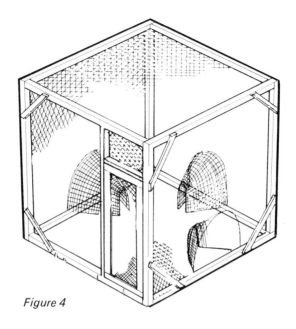

Figure 4

level funnel similar to that on a pheasant catcher is put in three sides with a door in the fourth. The funnels should be about 50cm wide by 50cm high on the outside, tapering to 10cm wide by 12cm high at the inner end, with a length of about 60cm (Figure 4). Some keepers dislike this type of trap since it occasionally catches the odd gamebird.

The trap can be run in one of two ways. Either by introducing food, water and several decoys as soon as it is set, or by pre-baiting. In the latter method no decoy is used and the trap is simply set up in an area where there are flock living corvids, with the roof off and the door open. Bait is then scattered both around and within the trap for several days until the corvids are coming with confidence. White sliced bread is often as good a bait as any. It is palatable and visible, and if the wrappers are left in the trap the area has an uncanny resemblance to a picnic site! Once the bait is disappearing regularly, close the door and fit the roof (a small piece of rearing-pen netting will do) and leave the trap for a full day. Daily catches in excess of 100 birds, particularly of rooks and jackdaws, are quite commonplace.

Sometimes it pays to leave a few birds as decoys for a second day but in most cases it is better to return to pre-baiting for another week. Once catches fall off it usually pays to move the trap to a new site.

Ladder Letterbox Traps

This type of cage is usually built to the same dimensions as the ground level funnel type. It has no particular advantage, except that there is no risk of catching gamebirds. Its main disadvantage is when using it to trap jackdaws, which seem to have an uncanny ability to escape through roof entrances, although this design reduces that to a minimum. As will be seen from Figure 5, the roof slopes from

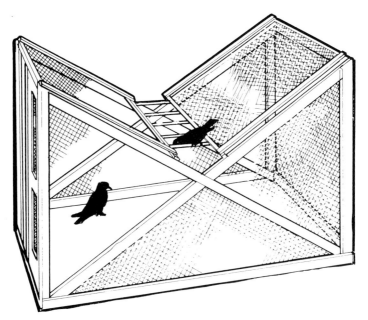

Figure 5

28

two sides to a central slot which has rungs across it like a ladder. The best size of slot is 14cm wide, with the rungs placed 9cm apart except for the centre which is 14cm square. The 30cm or so at each end is blocked off with netting to prevent jackdaws from climbing up the sides and escaping.

It is used in exactly the same ways as the ground level funnel type.

Destroying Corvid Nests

It is perfectly legal to destroy nests as part of a corvid control programme. Many keepers like to push out old corvid nests when drey poking for grey squirrels in early spring. This is certainly helpful in allowing the keeper to spot easily any new nests being built on his beat. Care must be taken, however, as it is an offence to damage the nests of birds of prey. Sitting corvids often stay on the nest when approached, and it is sometimes possible to shoot them.

CHAPTER FIVE

Avian Predators by Species

Magpie

The magpie is a serious egg predator whose population is growing throughout Europe. In Britain the Larsen trap has revolutionised its control, and is likely to remain the favoured method for many years to come. Non-breeding magpies rarely form the concentrations noticed for other corvids, so multi-catch cages are not very important, although the ground level funnel type is particularly applicable where needed.

Shooting also plays its part and is especially helpful for those D-I-Y or part-time keepers who cannot check traps daily. Magpies will come both to magpie decoys and to mob the large plastic owl decoys which are available. Using these, a well-hidden Gun can often account for several birds in a day. Waiting in this way is likely to produce more offers than creeping around with a shotgun, no matter how carefully it is done.

Rifles can play a part in magpie control too, always bearing in mind that one needs an absolutely safe background for a shot. In America the sport of 'varminting' is very popular. This usually involves using .22 or even .17 centre-fire rifles with very light-weight bullets at around 50 grains. This gives very high degrees of accuracy and makes magpies at up to 100m range a worthwhile shot. Shots at longer range than this should not be taken, as near-missed birds become very jumpy.

Crow

As with magpies, the Larsen trap has revolutionised crow control. In this case, however, non-breeding flocks are more likely to be a problem. This, and crows foraging out onto grouse moors or other large areas of open country, means that multi-catch cages are more likely to play a part.

Crows may be shot using the same techniques as those described for magpies. However, shooting over decoys and at large communal late-winter roosts can also play a more significant part. Where the magpie shooter does well to get two or three birds in a day, bags of 30 to 50 crows over decoys, and up to 20 per Gun at roosts, are quite normal. Such shooting does rely on the best possible use of concealment. Crows are very wary of the gun, so you must keep absolutely still until the last moment before you mount your gun and shoot.

Rook

Rooks can cause serious losses to game during the nesting season, particularly where nests are exposed or are in open situations. At The Game Conservancy's former experimental game farm, the pheasant laying pens were for some time raided by birds from a rookery three miles away. At least 150 eggs were found in the pens, broken and sucked by the rooks, and hundreds of others were carried off. More than one game farmer has found it worthwhile to buy laying-pen roof netting – the eggs saved from corvids have soon repaid the cost.

The adult rook can be cage trapped in much the same way as flock living crows, and some useful suggestions will be found in Chapter Three. But as prevention is better than cure, a more fundamental way is to go for the rookeries, which can be thinned out.

Ropes of bird-scaring bangers, hung as high as possible in the rookery trees, and giving out loud reports every 20 minutes will cause the birds to desert. During a frosty night at the right time of year this method can prevent rook eggs from hatching. The rope of 'bangers' should be hauled up into the treetops inside an oil drum from which the bottom has been removed. This will prevent rain from damping the fuse and also amplify the detonations. Bird scaring cannons, widely used in the fields, are not likely to be so effective at ground level near a rookery.

During the second and third weeks of May, before the foliage gets too dense, the fledgling rooks or 'branchers' may be shot. Because they are not fully fledged, this may be done with a .22 rifle. In this way a rookery can be thinned. Rook shooting used to be almost a traditional country sport in England, and shooting the 'branchers' with a modern accurate rifle and a telescopic sight is a humane and inexpensive way of checking an increase in this population.

It can also be possible to shoot rooks over decoys or crops, especially in favoured feeding areas and near refuse tips. As with all decoy shooting of wild birds, careful selection of site and concealment of guns is essential. All corvids are wary and sharp-eyed. A dead rook set on a pigeon flapper can add to the attractiveness of a decoy pattern.

Jackdaw

No countryman would be without the friendly jackdaw – indeed his clowning and "clacking" is as much a part of a summer's day as the cawing of the rooks. Yet these birds often need to be controlled, and the gamekeeper or farmer must be ready to do this speedily and humanely when necessary. Not only are jackdaws expert at stealing eggs from laying pens, they will also rob wild nests with great perseverance. For example, jackdaws disturbed or destroyed 28 partridge nests out of 32 in one 300 acre Lincolnshire park! Jackdaws have also been known to kill gamebird chicks and ducklings.

Apart from shooting, cage trapping is the main method of control. Use similar systems to those described for rooks.

Jay

The jay is one of those creatures that are not as black as they are painted. The odd pair of jays here and there are useful sentries on a shoot, giving a keeper warning of undesirable visitors. Also, many of the jays which are shot in winter are migrants from northern Europe which would not be around during the gamebird nesting season.

Though no one will deny that the jay is fond of the eggs and chicks of game and song birds, in a five-year period on The Game Conservancy's experimental estate we caught only one jay red-handed – shot beside a pheasant's nest from which it had taken two eggs. This said, there *are* instances of egg and chick predation by jays.

Jays can sometimes be caught in large cage traps designed for jackdaws, though smaller ones on the pheasant-catcher principle,

The jay can be a problem on some shoots, and can be caught in Larsen traps during the spring. (Photo: Hans Schouten)

about 1m square and 0.6m high, are more effective. They can also be caught in squirrel traps baited with maize, and jays can be caught in the same way as crows and magpies using Larsen traps.

Gulls

On most lowland shoots gulls are not a problem, but herring and both species of black-backed gulls can often be found quartering grouse moors for food, taking well-grown grouse chicks. Waterfowl breeding on wetlands near the coast can also be very vulnerable if there are gull colonies nearby. All three species can be shot, with a small calibre rifle, and the 'varminting' technique described under 'Magpies' has particular application when they are present on the ground. They can also be caught in multi-catch traps in much the same way as crows.

Moorhen and Coot

The moorhen or waterhen can be very troublesome on a shoot if allowed to become too numerous. These birds greedily eat the food put down for pheasants, partridge or duck, graze winter corn, damage watercress beds and sometimes take eggs, game chicks and ducklings.

Coot can sometimes be a nuisance to breeding ducks through egg eating or causing disturbance; they can also be aggressive to young wildfowl and have been known to eat ducklings. Both species can be shot quite easily, or caught alive in baited cage traps with funnel entrances. Pheasant catchers are also suitable, but remember that moorhens and coots are protected from 1 February to 31 August in Great Britain.

Starling

While starlings are clearly not game predators, they roost together in their thousands and are not infrequently a major nuisance to municipal authorities and forestry officials. Occasionally they will ruin a pheasant covert, fouling the ground with their droppings, which can destroy all ground cover and sometimes even kill the trees. Many methods of evicting them have been tried, including the emission of sound waves, ultra-violet rays, electrified wires, explosive bird-scaring ropes, bonfires, sulphur fumes, fireworks, stuffed birds, and so on. Sulphur fumes have on occasions been successful, as well as 'Thunderflash' rockets, especially when combined with playing tape recordings of starling distress calls. The rockets are set by daylight, being angled to explode just above the trees, and the first one is fired as soon as the starlings have settled down again after being disturbed, and so on. After three or more consecutive nights of the rocket treatment, the starlings usually desert the roost. It is believed that the whistling effect of the rocket disturbs the birds more than the explosive.

Anyone faced with a starling problem should contact their local Forestry Commission Wildlife Division for advice on how to control them.

CHAPTER SIX

Trapping Small Mammalian Predators

Harmful Species

Rats, mink and feral ferrets are the only species which should be rigorously controlled at every opportunity: other predators require more selective measures. Foxes are probably the most serious game predator on a national scale. They may be the subject of all-out attack in some districts, but in areas where a hunt is operating the campaign should be judicious. Stoats will take nesting hens, eggs and chicks, and weasels certainly kill a few partridge chicks. They can be controlled by tunnel trapping. The grey squirrel is in many senses more a pest of forestry than a game predator, but since it damages game coverts it often falls to the lot of the keeper to control it. Lastly, the feral cat is a serious and sometimes under-rated pest in many areas.

The Trapping Network

The basic defence against small ground predators consists of a strategic network of tunnel sites for trapping all over a shoot, particularly round the boundaries. On a beat of up to 1000ha (2500 acres), where the fields are of normal size and where there are sufficient hedges, stone walls, banks or ditches, a good keeper will wish to operate at least 100 traps from late winter to midsummer. The most critical time for predator control is the early spring when gamebirds are nesting. In practice, we find that 100 tunnels are often as much as a keeper can look after effectively, whatever the size of his beat, so one keeper will find it very difficult to trap thoroughly a beat

36

larger than 1200ha (3000 acres). In these circumstances it is all the more important to choose priority areas and the best catching places for every trap, and to cover the boundaries as well as possible.

For the part-time keeper who, perhaps, can find a couple of hours each morning to check his traps, the best policy is to choose a good area with a high potential to produce wild game and trap it well. This is more likely to produce results than a sprinkling of traps over a wide area which only take a small proportion of predators.

Tunnel Traps

Tunnel traps are simply traps set in natural or artificial tunnels situated in the normal thoroughfares of ground predators. Gin-traps are now illegal and humane spring traps such as the Fenn have taken their place. The Imbra and similar rabbit traps are rather too large for ordinary tunnels, and require divided tunnels (tunnels made in

The Fenn Mk IV is probably the most popular tunnel trap.

two halves, which are separated for setting). These divided tunnels are normally too fiddly and time-consuming for the busy keeper. The law requires that all approved tunnel traps must be set in tunnels.

For catching in tunnels the Fenn rat trap (Mark IV) is now well tried, and may be obtained from Mr A Fenn, FHT Works, High Street, Astwood Bank, Redditch, Worcs., or from Game Conservancy Ltd's Sales Centre. The Springer 4 is very similar and can be obtained from A B Country Products, Troy Industrial Estate, Jill Lane, Sambourne, nr Astwood Bank, Redditch, Worcs., B96 6ES. Both traps are also widely available from game management and agricultural suppliers.

The tunnels can be made of a wooden frame (bark off-cuts are suitable) covered with turf, or of large stones, bricks, drainpipes, bales of straw, weathered pitch fibre pipes, faggot piles and so on. The minimum length of the tunnels should be 45cm and they should be just large enough inside to allow the trap to be sprung freely. Excessively large tunnels can allow the trap to jump and throw its victim free. Natural sites, such as the roots of trees, can equally well be used. Apart from the ordinary 'run-through' tunnel, blind tunnels may be constructed with no exit; these can be made in grass banks. In East Anglia the wellams (pipes carrying ditches under gateways) make ideal trapping sites even when there is a little water running. The rough grass beside wire fences is also a good trapping place – especially where new plantations are enclosed and the tunnels are made alongside or through the netting.

Useful portable tunnels can be made by nailing together three sawn planks of timber about 60cm long; inside measurements should be about 13cm high and 15cm wide at the base. A reserve supply of these wooden frames is most useful as the basis of quickly making good trapping tunnels.

How to Use Tunnel Traps

Tunnels are usually unbaited, as ground predators are naturally curious and will hunt almost any earthy hole. In the early spring

Tunnels should be just wide enough to take the trap with the safety catch off and just high enough to allow the jaws to close freely. (Note that these traps are shown in the tunnel entrance for clear viewing – they should be set well back into the tunnel.)

it may pay to put a flesh bait well inside the tunnel; rabbit liver is a favourite. In this case a trap should be set at both ends. If the trapper is lucky enough to catch a female stoat or weasel while in season, a few drops of its urine on the plate on any trap can be very attractive to any males.

Bitch weasels weigh very little and may not spring a Fenn trap unless lightly set. Some keepers prefer to file down the setting pin so that it catches 'light', ie with very little pressure on the plate. This can be a mistake. If not correctly done, it can ruin a trap.

In a wide, unkempt hedge, wings of turf, small-meshed wire-netting or other materials can be constructed to form a lead-in to the tunnel. Another similar and very telling practice is to make a short cut from the outside furrow in either field, leading to the centre of the hedge. If a stoat is travelling down this field furrow (as they often do) unless there is an intersecting furrow veering off to the centre of the hedge it will by-pass the trap. The turf dug out of this

Gaps in hedges make good trapping sites.

furrow should be banked up on top to make it even more difficult to climb out.

Runways into traps should be kept clear of heavy weed growth by regular hoeing. Alternatively one treatment with a total weedkiller should ensure that the trapping runways remain open all summer, but it must not be overdone or the traps will be left exposed for all to see.

In areas of rough, tussocky grass, where ground predators have no obvious travel lane such as hedge or bank, a straight furrow may be ploughed right across open ground in order to form an artificial run for stoats and weasels. Such a furrow will almost certainly become a regular runway if it is kept clear, and will be easy to trap. Wheel-ruts made during a wet spell may also prove useful in providing runs.

A well-planned trap round should lead the keeper along almost every hedge and into every copse on his beat. Even if he is taking

Having chosen a suitable site for your trap, dig out a trench in which to place the tunnel.

Bed the trap carefully into the tunnel so that it cannot rock. Then cover the tunnel with turf or logs to disguise it from vandals, and restrict the entrance with a pair of stout sticks.

only an occasional stoat or rat from six dozen traps, he will at the same time be covering his ground very thoroughly and should miss nothing of importance that may be going on. This is almost as important as controlling the pests. He will see the farm staff and others about the shoot daily; he will pass winter feeding stations or pheasant catchers according to the time of year; he will make a note of partridge pairs and the distribution of wild pheasants. If he is a young person gaining experience, this regular round will help him to become a first-class naturalist and field detective. He will learn to spot the presence of unwelcome predators and take appropriate action before serious damage occurs.

Every keeper will have his own particular way of setting traps. Before being used, new traps should be buried in the earth or weathered until they have lost their factory smell and shine. Better still, they should be degreased by boiling in water with washing up liquid and skimming off the scum which rises. They can then be tanned by boiling with oak bark, or in tea. Some keepers then wax their traps both to prevent them from rusting and to make them

43

spring more smoothly. Gloves are not necessary but a trapper's hand should be free from any obviously unsuitable smells – soap or tobacco, for instance! A good rubbing with earth helps remove such odours. Some game keepers use gloves anyway to avoid handling rats which can present a disease risk (especially Weil's disease). When setting the trap, the securing chain should be buried and the soil made firm all round the tunnel entrance. The chain should always be pegged down or, in the case of wooden tunnels, be stapled to the side of the tunnel. The trap itself should be placed sufficiently far back inside to avoid danger to dogs or game investigating the entrance, and be bedded down so that the plate is about level with the ground. It is largely a matter of personal preference whether the plate is covered or not. The tunnel entrances must be made smaller by sinking two or more sticks firmly in the ground across the entrance – leaving a gap just large enough for stoats and rats to enter, but preventing birds from being caught. To ensure a clean kill it is important that the predator enters the tunnel directly from the front, and not from the side of the entrance.

Traps must be examined daily by law and should be reset fre-

All traps must be checked at least once a day.

New traps may need adjustment. In this case the plate needs to be bent down-
wards as shown below to allow it to set horizontally.

quently, whether they have caught anything or not. If resetting is neglected, the working parts may get blocked by mud, leaves or grit, and the trap will fail to catch. It always pays to check that the safety-catch is 'off' after setting a trap!

Among the predators which can be *continually* caught by a good coverage of tunnel traps are rats, stoats, weasels, grey squirrels and mink.

Box Trapping

The Continental box trap is a wooden tunnel with a see-saw in it which is employed much like a tunnel trap. The Game Conservancy carried out trials some years ago with these little portable wooden tunnels, and learned to get good results with them. We also asked for comments from some very experienced trappers in France, Holland, Denmark and Germany, where these traps have been used for generations. Our combined suggestions are set down briefly below.

There are basically three sizes of box traps, varying from those over 1m in length, designed to catch poaching cats and larger mammals, to the smallest ones 0.5m long, for rats, stoats and weasels. The entrance end of the tunnel is usually about 9cm × 11cm with the roof sloping up to 20cm at the far end. Inside is a see-saw, pivoting on a metal spindle, which tips up as the animal runs into the box – the see-saw remaining locked in the 'closed' position behind the animal. At the far end the tunnel is covered with a metal grille.

It is important that the wood is properly seasoned and does not swell, or the see-saw will jam in wet weather. Creosote should *not* be used as a preservative, as it is likely to keep vermin away for a long time until the smell has completely worn off. New white wood is also a disadvantage.

Small ground vermin enter these box traps for exactly the same reason that they enter tunnel traps, ie in search of prey, and to take shelter quickly in what looks like a convenient bolt hole. Normally the traps are not baited – and if they are they soon acquire the smell

Box traps can be good for weasels and stoats, especially if baited with a few grains of corn to attract mice.

of the many mice they are always catching – but, as in tunnel trapping, refinements (if one may use the word) such as the contents of a bitch weasel's bladder are often used with advantage.

Box traps can be used singly but are also effective if used in pairs, side by side, with an entrance facing either way. They can be put in exactly the same sort of place as a conventional tunnel trap. A certain degree of camouflage around the entrance may be advisable, to prevent curious people from pulling them out and possibly stealing them. The box should, however, slide easily in and out of its tunnel – if it is being used in that way – and not have too many flints or turves placed directly on top of it, otherwise the tunnel will have to be reconstructed every time it catches.

Some of the best places include the following: on small, used paths in spinneys and copses (blocking the path on either side with brushwood or a similar obstruction so that the animal is forced to go through the middle); on a plank over a stream; in the boundary furrow of a field, often used by stoats when the hedgebank is very wet; in the field ditch or the hedge; between two farm crops, if separated by a track; in a pile of flints in the corner of a field; beside a barn or a wall, and on rafters in old farm buildings; in hay and straw stacks; alongside a wire-netting fence or a pheasant pen; in the centre of the rough grass under a downland wire fence; half-hidden in a pile of cut logs in covert; or in a dry drain or culvert.

It is advisable to carry a small stout bag on the trapping round in which to tip the captive, so that it can be killed humanely and without risk of escaping or biting.

The Game Conservancy gives its full support to the Government's ongoing campaign to stop the illegal poisoning of wildlife. The campaign slogan is "Legal Pest Control – Yes; Illegal Poisoning – No". The Government increasingly recognises the need for legitimate traps and other control techniques, but every right-minded individual and organisation condemns law breaking and cruelty. In the past, incidents of deliberate, illegal poisoning by a small minority of gamekeepers have done untold damage to the good name of game conservation.

STOP ILLEGAL

POISONING

OF OUR WILDLIFE

A joint campaign by Government and other concerned organisations

Predator control is an essential part of successful shoot management.

The carrion crow is a serious predator of gamebird nests.

Larsen traps are an effective and highly selective method of control for magpies and crows.

Multi-catch cages are particularly useful for controlling flock living corvids.

The rifle is a valuable tool for controlling a wide range of game predators.

Fenn traps in tunnels are a good method of controlling stoats and rats.

Mink cages set beside pheasant release pens are a valuable insurance against mass kills of poults.

CHAPTER SEVEN

Fox Control

Foxhunting is an important field sport in Britain and the gamekeeper should be sensitive to the needs of the hunt as well as his shoot. Indeed, many shooting men are also devoted to hunting. While in this book we are solely concerned with the protection of gamebirds, we would not advocate measures which might interfere with hunting. Although there is no doubt that the fox is one of the most important predators of game, especially at nesting time, its control in relation to hunting and other local conditions is a matter which must be carefully considered. Good co-operation exists in

Good co-operation between hunting and shooting interests is a vital part of rural life. (Photo: BFSS)

many areas where hunting and shooting are both important amenities of the countryside.

Foxes are, however, increasing in number in many places and in some of those, ranging from common land in the suburbs to Highland glens, hunting with hounds is impossible. They are also populating areas like the Fens where previously there were virtually no foxes at all. In most districts it will be necessary to control their populations by other methods as well as hunting.

In practice, most foxhunters accept the keepers' need to control foxes; their concern is much more about access to the countryside. 'No go' areas where they are not allowed even to run through mean large 'buffer zones' which cannot be hunted. Allowing the hunt to run through if they meet nearby is unlikely to cause much disturbance provided that it does not happen on a shooting day.

Our research has shown that on land without gamekeepers, nest predation by foxes is such a potent factor that the gamebird population can be reduced to a very low level.

Fox Snaring

The control of foxes is the most contentious aspect of the gamekeeper's programme, yet the proper use of snares by gamekeepers is an essential element of this. No single method of control is likely to be adequate on its own, and a range of techniques will usually be needed. Every effort must be made to ensure that where snaring is done, it is carried out as humanely as possible and captured animals are killed swiftly and painlessly. In addition, snares should not be set so that they are likely to catch an unintended victim.

The ordinary fox snare consists of a heavy wire loop set in a place where a fox is liable to pass (Figure 5). The free end is tethered in some way and the loop is designed to close around the neck. Various adaptations have been made to the ordinary loop in order to increase its effectiveness. A simple and important modification is to put a bend in the wire at the place where the loop begins. This

50

Fitting a stop to prevent tight closure of snares removes the risk of catching deer by their feet.

helps to prevent the loop accidentally becoming too big and causing the animal to be captured round the chest or waist. A swivel must be attached between the loop and tether, and the snare's eye should be made with a metal ring or loop rather than a slip knot in the wire.

Fitting a stop to the snare about 20cm to 25cm from the eye prevents the snare from closing to a loop tighter than about 6cm diameter. This is a great help in preventing larger animals such as deer from being caught by the foot. On many commercially made snares the stop, which is in the form of a coil of soft wire, is free to slide, and should be fitted by the user. The easiest way to do this is to hold the snare against some form of anvil and tap it firmly with a hammer. This squashes in into place.

Snares should not be set near public footpaths or in other places where their use may cause offence or risk the capture of dogs while they are under reasonable control, or in the vicinity of houses. Fox snares should always be lifted when there is a meet of foxhounds in the area.

51

Successful snaring, like tunnel trapping, is very much a matter of attention to detail. Degreasing and colouring of snares in the way described on page 43 makes a significant difference to the catch rate. Many keepers now take this one stage further by spraying their snares with dull green paint to make them less visible. The standard fox snare is set about 15cm above ground with a loop 15cm high by 20cm wide supported by a wooden tealer. A problem with this system is that standard snares are apt to spring open again if a fox backs off quickly, allowing it to escape. To help overcome this The Game Conservancy introduced a snare made of softer, less springy wire.

Studies on snaring and discussions with professional fox trappers indicate that perhaps most snares are set too low. A slightly larger pear-shaped noose, hung from above on a tealer made of 4mm fence wire, and set with its lower edge some 20cm to 25cm high is proving very successful. This is especially so if the eye itself has a little more weight than usual, as this also tends to cause the snare to continue closing rather than springing back open when it starts to draw (see photo). When such snares are properly camouflaged they are very difficult to see, and can be used in much more open situations than many keepers are used to. Livestock paths (provided there are no stock in the field concerned), cereal tramlines, field headlands and open woodland tracks can all be productive. One advantage of these sites is that foxes are often moving fairly quickly, and are therefore more cleanly caught than when snaring in hedges or thick cover. Also, since there is nothing nearby to entangle the captive, there is less danger of it being harmed, which is important especially for the infrequent non-target animal that may be taken. Snaring in such open situations requires a firm peg. One suitable choice for most soils is a 40cm length of 1″ angle iron driven down to ground level, to which the snare is tethered. It is vital to remember exactly where these have been put, and lever them out of the ground when snaring ceases, so that they do not pose a threat to agricultural machinery.

Another useful refinement, especially for late winter, is to rub the snares with beeswax. This makes them run more freely, and also sheds rain which can otherwise freeze on in droplets in cold weather and stop them for just long enough for a fox to escape.

The rocking eye snare, which is a registered design, closes quickly under its own weight, thus reducing the risk of foxes backing out.

Well designed snares with wire tealers can be set in surprisingly open situations.

54

The availability of areas suitable for setting snares is often limited by the presence of livestock. Upland areas in particular have sheep present all the year round, and in such situations snares should be set within fenced middens. There has long been a tradition of setting snares around recently buried animals since the corpse attracts the attention of foxes. This idea has been developed further by keepers in southern Scotland to make an effective method of fox control where stock is present. An area of thick vegetation is chosen in a place where foxes are known to run; a patch of rushes near the confluence of two rivers is often ideal. A grave is dug and a dead sheep, deer gralloch or other carrion such as fish offal is buried. The grave is fenced with 50 metres of sheep fencing but is not secured closely to the ground so the foxes can slip under the fence. Between five and seven paths are then carefully cut with secateurs or a strimmer to lead the foxes in towards the grave. Care should be taken in cutting these paths, and they should lead from the natural fox runs/ sheep paths outside the fence in towards the grave. The principle is to guide the foxes in to the grave and then place 20 or more snares on the paths within the midden. Some estates have had great success with this technique close to large forestry blocks, and every midden we have monitored has caught at least one fox.

Fox Driving

Properly and efficiently carried out, this technique can be effective in accounting for foxes which lie out in the open. However, badly executed operations usually lead to poor results. Fox driving is most successful in late winter and early spring when there is least cover.

Co-ordination between teams of Guns and beaters is very important, so each party should include at least one person who knows exactly how the drive is to be carried out. Guns and beaters should be briefed well away from the covert to be driven, and the standing Guns should all be without dogs; these are usually unnecessary with the beaters as well, and certainly no foxy looking animals should be used!

Guns should line out downwind of the area to be driven, without any talking. When driving open deciduous woodland, Guns should be no more than 40 metres apart, facing into the covert with their backs to a tree. A Gun on each flank of the beating line, or even having all the beaters armed, should prevent any fox going back. Having allowed time for standing Guns to line out, the beaters should move steadily through the wood, tapping with sticks but not shouting. In this way foxes are not unduly startled, and should move forward slowly, well ahead of the line, so that they present safe, easy and close shots. Once the drive is under way, the walking Guns can shoot other pests without upsetting the chances of killing foxes.

In very thick cover, especially young conifer plantations, it will be necessary to shoot foxes as they cross rides. To do this safely the Guns should not be more than 35 metres apart, and should stand up to the edge of the wood, facing the back of their neighbour and only shooting foxes as they cross the ride in front of them. Again the beaters should advance reasonably slowly, using their sticks freely, and not shouting. The foxes should then cross the rides quite slowly, presenting safe and simple shots (see Figure 6).

With both these methods there should be no need for long-range shots, and fairly small shot sizes between 3 and 5 have been found to produce clean kills. The larger sizes up to SSG, which are often used, can result in very dangerous ricochets, as well as wounding rather than killing of foxes due to the poor pattern which they offer.

In large forestry blocks in Scotland and Wales packs of hounds bred specially for the purpose are sometimes used to move foxes to carefully positioned standing Guns. With good local knowledge the most likely 'exits' can be covered with a fairly small team of Guns.

Fox Calling and Lamping

Foxes can be brought within range of shotgun or rifle by calling. Some people can imitate the sound of a squealing rabbit or hare to attract foxes. For those who are unable to do so various metal

Safe fox driving in dense young conifers.

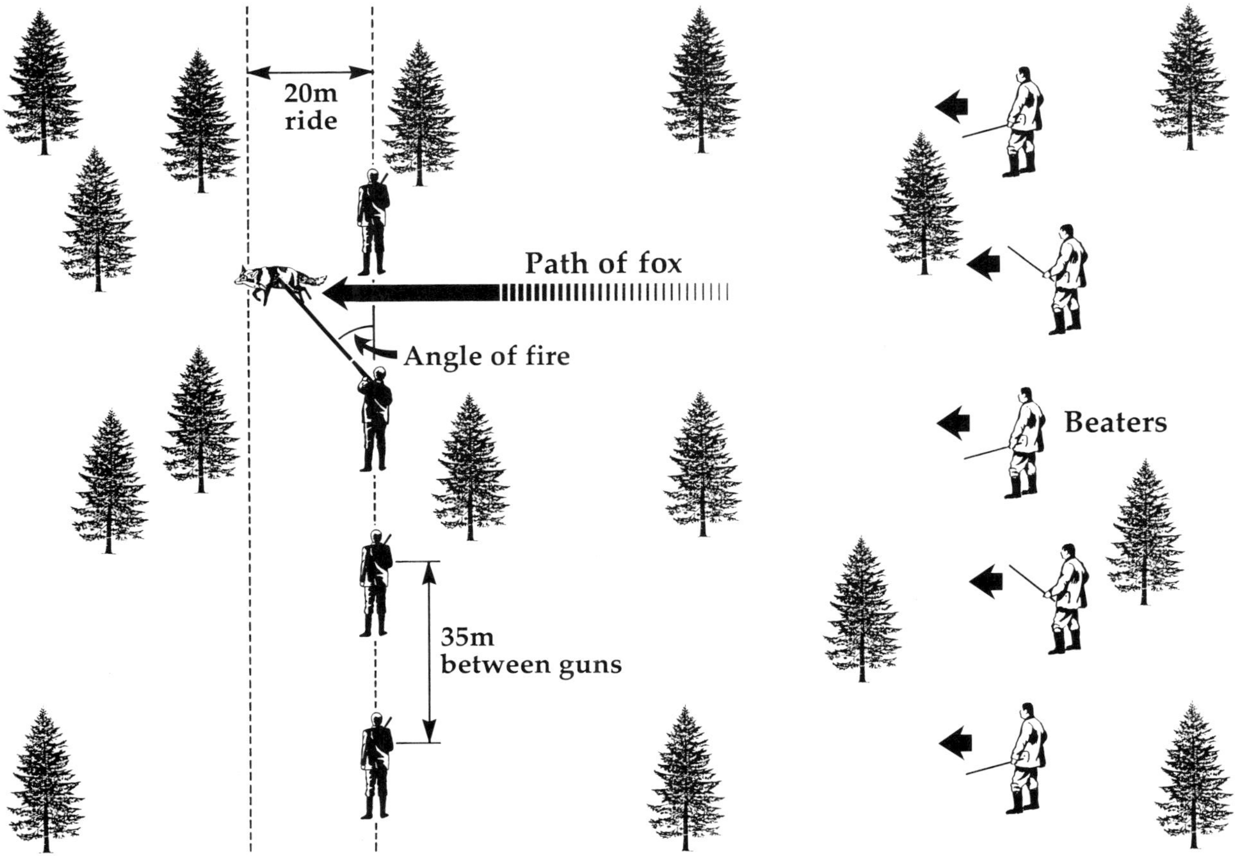

Beaters

Path of fox

Angle of fire

20m ride

35m between guns

Figure 6

57

and plastic calls can be purchased, some of which produce an effective call. Home-made calls are often better than those on the market. A piece of polystyrene rubbed against a vehicle windscreen can often produce an enticing squeak.

Calling at dawn and dusk can be very successful, and after dark foxes will often come readily to the squeak, even when a torch is used for illumination. The general technique for calling at night is to approach an area from the downwind side where it is thought that one or more foxes are hunting. A few rabbit squeal sounds should be made. After a pause of 2–5 minutes the ground area should be scanned with the lamp. If a fox or its eyes are picked up in the beam, calling should recommence. Only the bottom of the beam should play on the animal so that the foreground is not illuminated. Depending on the wariness of the fox, and the skill of the caller, the animal may come very close, ie to within 10 or 15 metres. Adult foxes will often circle 70–100m away in which case only a rifle should be used by a competent marksman. For heavy rifles high velocity loads are available with suitable bullets for foxes. Cubs can usually be called-up within shotgun range. Some foxes, especially if they have been shot at before, will be frightened by a call. If you suspect that such a fox is around it may be best to shine the light first before squeaking.

Safety is *always* important. It is vital that the ground is known intimately. In experienced hands a powerful lamp, an effective call and an accurate shot can be a most humane method of fox control.

The beginner is advised to spend a night with someone experienced before trying fox calling himself.

Fox Earths and Terriers

Now that it is illegal to gas foxes in their earths, more keepers are turning to use of terriers to control cubbing earths. It is important to remember that while it is perfectly legal to enter terriers to foxes, any use of terriers in badger setts is illegal. Unfortunately, with growing populations of both species in most areas, the frequency of co-habitation is increasing. Gamekeepers and others with problems must apply to their MAFF regional office for a licence if they wish to disturb badger setts to control foxes.

Feral Cats

The feral poaching cat ranks very high as a destroyer of nesting game, and often young chicks as well. A Working Party on the control of predatory mammals, with representatives of all shades of opinion from conservation, agriculture and game management groups, described the feral cat as a "menace to wildlife".

When using a rifle or shotgun, early morning is the best time to deal with feral cats. Otherwise they may be caught live in various types of large cage trap.

CHAPTER EIGHT

Other Mammals

Rats

It would seem almost unnecessary to describe the rat as a pest, but there is a surprisingly large number of people who do not realise how much damage this animal can cause. Experience on a wild partridge or pheasant beat during the nesting season would quickly dispel any doubts. In addition, rats will consume large quantities of food put out for gamebirds and may kill chicks on the rearing

Tunnel traps take significant numbers of rats.

field and pheasant and partridge poults in the release pen. On some estates feed hoppers and maize strips, planted especially for shooting, may actually contribute towards maintaining the local rat population through the winter. It cannot be stressed enough that, from both the farming and shooting points of view, rats must be properly controlled at all times. Systematic treatment with poisoned bait and tunnel trapping at all strategic places should be undertaken, and the campaign never relaxed. Clearance from an area is only temporary and re-infestation usually occurs quickly.

Rats can spread serious diseases including leptospirosis, salmonellosis and foot and mouth. About 40% of all rats carry leptospiral bacteria at some time during their lives. Every precaution should be taken to protect the skin when handling dead rats or anything that could be contaminated with rat urine; thick gloves will prove useful. The leptospiral bacteria cause a jaundice known as Weil's disease which can be fatal in humans and dogs. The following notes on rat control have been prepared by the Ministry of Agriculture, Fisheries and Food, and are reproduced by kind permission of HMSO.

Control of Rats with Anticoagulants

The most efficient method of controlling rats is by poison baiting using one of the anticoagulant poisons. Seven of these compounds are now available, warfarin (many proprietary names), coumatetralyl (Racumin 57), chlorophacinone (Drat), difenacoum (Neosorexa or Ratak), bromodialone (Slaymor), brodifacoum and flocoumafen. All except brodifacoum and flocoumafen are available through retail outlets; the sale of the latter two is at present restricted to professional users and to persons occupying industrial or commercial premises.

The anticoagulant poisons are effective because they work slowly and rats continue to feed until they die, usually in a few days. When poison baiting, it is vital to ensure that the rats can eat the succession of daily doses that are necessary to cause death. This can only be achieved by first putting bait in as many places as possible so that the rats can find it easily and do not have to compete with each other for it. Secondly the baits need regular replenishment so that the rats can continue to feed on them each day. If this is not done, rats may recover from the effects of the poison.

The anticoagulant poisons can now normally only be bought already mixed with cereal in a ready-to-use form.

Method of Baiting with Anticoagulant Poisons

Before starting to bait it is worth looking carefully around the infested area to find out how extensive it is and also, from the traces of infestation (rat holes, runs, fresh droppings, foot prints, etc.), where the rats are most numerous and active. It is essential to know the full extent of the infestation so as to bait every part of it, because if parts are not baited the rats in them very quickly re-infest the successfully treated areas. It is also necessary to find out from the traces where the rats are living, running and feeding in order to lay baits to the best advantage.

In places where rat traces are plentiful one should aim to lay 100g to 200g piles of bait in holes not more than 2m to 3m apart beside defined runs, near walls and wherever rats are likely to find them. As rats naturally prefer to travel by sheltered routes, baits should be laid also in all sheltered places, and exposed baits should be covered with any material that is available. Corrugated iron or asbestos sheets, tiles and bricks can be used for this purpose. The cover provided in this way not only encourages the rats to feed but protects the baits from the weather, wild birds and farmstock. If the ground is damp, the piles of bait should be laid on pieces of wood, tin, stone, tile, slate or plastic.

Where traces of rats are less plentiful the piles of bait need not be laid so close together. Nevertheless, as a general rule, a number of small (100g) piles will be more effective than one large one in any area in which rats are active. A few baits should also be laid outside the obviously infested area because rats tend constantly to explore new territory. Baits placed in this way also help to poison rats that may attempt to move into the area being treated.

If, out of doors, suitable sheltered sites for baits cannot be found, land drain tiles or lengths of pitch fibre or plastic pipes 600mm long by 100mm diameter may be used. Rats, however, do not readily enter containers to eat bait and it may take a week or more for them to do so.

Rats are naturally cautious and will not feed on bait immediately. Some bait is eaten on the first night that it is down, but more will be taken the next night and probably more on the third. The baits should therefore be replenished on the third day. Wherever a pile of bait has been completely eaten, double the amount of bait should be put back.

The poison begins to have an effect after three or four days and the bait consumption should begin to decrease, but the baits should still be replenished every three to five days, particularly in the areas in which a lot has been eaten, until takes of bait cease altogether. This may take from two to four weeks, depending on the nature of the infestation and the thoroughness of the baiting. Then the holes should be filled in and a few days later a check should be made for survivors by looking for reopened holes and fresh droppings. If any are found more poison, preferably in a different bait, should be laid in the areas in which they occur.

Permanent Baiting

When a farm has been cleared of rats, permanent baiting points placed in strategic places round the farm and farm buildings serve to deal with new invaders and prevent the build up of large infestations. Weatherproof bait containers that hold at least 1kg of bait can be made from boxes, drain pipes or oil drums. These should be checked every month or so and kept topped up with bait. It is a good idea to use bait sachets made by sealing 500g in a polythene bag so that it stays fresh. Rats love to chew plastics anyway, and will soon break in when they colonise. The build up of infestations

After clearing an infestation sealed sachets of poison can be placed in rat holes to deal with any re-colonisation.

can also be prevented by clearing up any rubbish that offers the rodents harbourage both inside and outside the buildings. Feeding stuffs and grain can be protected from rats by proofing barns and stores and by keeping feed in metal bins.

Resistance to Anticoagulants

Some infestations do not respond to anticoagulant treatments within the normal time of two to four weeks. **These failures are usually the result of using too little bait or of putting it in too few places, or of using bait that does not attract all the rats away from their nor-**

mal feed. It sometimes happens, however, that animals survive because they are able to eat anticoagulants without being killed. Such resistant animals reveal themselves by continuing to eat relatively large amounts of bait each day, long after the treatment should have ended. In Britain anticoagulant resistant rats are found in a large area on the Welsh/English border, including the counties of Powys and Shropshire as well as parts of some neighbouring counties, and in an area comprising parts of Hampshire, Wiltshire, Berkshire and Oxfordshire. Isolated cases have also occurred in other parts of England. In Scotland, anticoagulant resistant rats are commonly found in the area between Edinburgh and Glasgow. When resistance to warfarin, coumatetralyl or chlorophacinone is suspected, difenacoum or bromodialone should be used to poison the rats. In those areas where difenacoum and bromodialone resistance is now present, there are two possibilities: to use calciferol (Sorexa CD) or zinc phosphide, or to call in a professional pest control operator.

When zinc phosphide is used it is important to remember that it is an acute poison and that a different baiting technique is needed. In this case users should pre-bait with the chosen cereal base without addition of poison for a week. Rats often prefer damp baits to dry ones, particularly in granaries, mills or meal stores where dry grain forms the staple diet and water is scarce. A very attractive bait to use with zinc phosphide in these situations is soaked wheat – that is, whole wheat which has been soaked for 48 hours in water and then had the surplus water drained off. Once this is disappearing regularly, the poison is mixed in the *same base*, and put down in place of the unpoisoned bait. When mixing anticoagulants be sure to wear proper protective clothing and a mask. It is good practice to lay zinc phosphide late in the evening, so that the rats have time to take a lethal dose undisturbed overnight. Rats which have had a sublethal dose can become bait-shy and very difficult to kill. All surplus bait and dead rats should be removed the following morning and buried or burned, thus avoiding any risk to gamebirds or other species.

Occasional bait-shy rats are a problem whichever poison is used.

They can form the nucleus of a new infestation. Operating a few well-sited tunnel traps can account for these survivors and help prevent re-infestation.

Safety Precautions

Though less dangerous than other rodenticides, anticoagulants are poisonous to both humans and other mammals. It is only sensible when handling poison baits to take care not to breathe in or otherwise absorb any poison. If you think you have absorbed any poison, or if you have any illness that you suspect is in any way related to handling of poisons, seek medical advice immediately. Unused poison bait should be kept safely locked away in a proper store and any buckets, spoons or scales that are used to mix or dispense bait should be washed after use. Pigs and dogs seem to be especially susceptible to anticoagulants, so it is essential either to keep all livestock away from the areas being treated or to protect the baits so that they can only be reached by rats. When a treatment is finished all uneaten bait should be recovered as far as practicable and burned or deeply buried. The bodies of dead rats should also be burned or buried.

Different anticoagulants have different toxicity both to rats and other wildlife. The first generation poisons (namely warfarin, coumatetralyl and chlorophasinone) are less poisonous than the second generation (difenacoum and bromodialone). Brodifacoum and flocoumafen (the third generation) are more toxic again. Thus, in areas where there is no anticoagulant resistance it is wise to choose a first generation poison even if it takes a little longer to kill the rats. This also reduces the risk to other wildlife which might eat a poisoned rat, particularly owls and other birds of prey.

Mink

Mink were introduced into Great Britain from North America in the 1920s and bred commercially for their fur. Due to accidental

66

Care in the choice of anticoagulants can reduce the risk of secondary poisoning, particularly of owls.

escapes, and deliberate releases when fur-farming became unprofitable, they became established in the wild and have now colonised nearly every river system in the country. There are still a few areas where mink are scarce or absent, but these are diminishing all the time.

Mink mate from February to April and the average litter is five to six, but larger numbers have been recorded. They have no natural predators, and as they can live for six to seven years the reason for their rapid spread in this country can be appreciated.

Although mink are usually found near water they are capable of making long overland journeys. Fish and frogs, ducks and other waterfowl, rabbits and gamebirds are taken by mink as well as domestic poultry, turkeys and geese. They are extremely agile in the water and are regarded as a potential threat to fishing and to

67

all riverside wildlife in this country. One of the signs of the presence of mink is a sudden decline in the number of moorhens and water voles on a particular stretch of water. Mink often kill in excess of their requirements. A keeper might find a store of fish hidden by a mink under a fallen tree, yet it hardly ever returns to the store. As many as three hundred pheasant poults have been killed in one night by mink in a release pen. Released ducks are also at particular risk.

Fortunately trapping with wire cage traps can be highly effective against mink. They do not appear to be particularly trap-shy and strong cage traps designed especially for mink are very successful. These may be baited with *fresh* fish, offal, chickens' heads or other animal remains. Mink are not normally carrion feeders, preferring to catch and kill their food, hence the need for fresh baits. Rotten remains may actually deter them, so unbaited cages are probably better, especially when they are covered to form dark, mysterious

Cage traps are particularly effective for mink.

holes for mink to investigate. Artificial scents or 'lures' are popular for mink in America, and some UK trappers import these. The best trapping sites are on river banks, preferably on a stretch of mud at the water's edge or under the bank itself, or in existing holes, culverts or logs. Once a good trap site has been discovered, mink will usually be taken there at intervals over a long period. Approved spring traps in tunnels will also take mink in the same places. Recent Game Conservancy research has shown that it pays to choose sites in high vegetation, and that the optimum trapping density is one per 70 metres of stream.

Mink caught in cage traps can be humanely destroyed with a low-powered air rifle, or by putting the whole trap into a plastic sack into which a pad soaked in carbon tetrachloride can be introduced. When unconscious, the mink can be extracted and despatched by a blow on the head.

As well as being good climbers, mink can squeeze through a hole

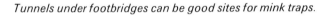

Tunnels under footbridges can be good sites for mink traps.

4cm in diameter, which makes them difficult to exclude. A careful watch should be kept for their distinctive and surprisingly large, star-shaped, five-toed tracks and every effort made to eliminate this serious pest.

There are many design features which can be incorporated into release pen plans which help to reduce the chance of a mink breaking in and causing a mass kill. These are discussed in Green Guide No 10, Gamebird Releasing.

Moles

From time to time moles accidentally disturb partridge nests. In one year on a single beat on The Game Conservancy's former experimental shoot, ten nests were upset by moles, though six were rebuilt by the watchful keeper. On another occasion 14 partridge eggs were recovered from a mole run.

Trapping with barrel and half-barrel mole traps requires a rather special touch, but a patent double-ended steel trap (sometimes called the Duffus) is also available which is much easier to set. (This is available from Quadtag Ltd., Hertford, Herts.) A. Fenn of Hooper's Lane, Astwood Bank, Redditch, Worcestershire, also makes a spring mole trap.

Poisoning with strychnine, using good-sized worms as bait, is probably the most effective method available for killing moles. But to learn how to do it, a personal demonstration by the local Pest Officer is better and safer than a few lines in a booklet. *In any case, the poison can only be obtained by applying to MAFF and proving evidence of mole damage .*

The keeper should be wary of mole runs which penetrate under rearing pens. They may allow weasels to enter and wreak havoc among the birds.

CHAPTER NINE

Grey Squirrels

Following introductions from America in the late 1800s, the grey squirrel's successful colonisation of Great Britain has been equally matched by its reputation as a pest.

Their main impact is through stripping the bark of trees, especially in the 5–15 year age class. They also cause considerable trouble to the gamekeeper through stealing food, damaging food hoppers, and taking occasional game eggs. Control methods are rather specialised, hence the inclusion of this section here.

The grey squirrel causes serious forestry damage, including game coverts. It can also take eggs, and steal food put out for game.

Grey squirrels live in nests or dreys which are 0.3m–0.9m in diameter, usually built in a tree fork 2.5m–15m above the ground. These dreys are roughly made of twigs in leaf and are usually lined with grass, leaves and honeysuckle bark. They remain in use for four to five years, and in winter may contain six or more squirrels at a time. In summer flimsier, temporary dreys or bowers are often made in the outside branches of trees up to 25m from the ground. *The red squirrel's dreys are made of leafless twigs and should be left untouched* .

Tunnel Trapping

The keeper who already has approved traps for catching ground predators can use them most effectively in tunnels against squirrels.

Tunnel traps using Fenn Mk IV traps can take significant numbers of grey squirrels.

Apart from the normal tunnel trap sites in woodland, which will catch occasional grey squirrels, hollow tree roots, dry drains, holes in banks, walls and hollow stumps can all be used. Areas of bare soil around the base of large trees are usually productive, also under the roots of a tree which has partly blown down to lie at an angle against its neighbours. Baiting is unnecessary if the traps can be set on natural runs, but a scatter of grain may increase catches, particularly when food is short in late winter, spring and early summer. This can also attract pheasants, so trap entrances must be well protected to avoid disasters.

Cage Trapping

Cage trapping is a most effective method of controlling grey squirrels, particularly in those areas where the use of warfarin is not allowed due to the presence of red squirrels. Cage traps should be set under trees known to be used by squirrels travelling between the canopy and the ground. Usually, large trees with boughs extending well down the trunk provide good sites.

Except where squirrels are accustomed to taking grain intended for pheasants, the best bait is whole maize. Squirrels tend to eat only the germ, and maize grains should be examined for this certain evidence of the presence of grey squirrels. When the traps are first put in position they should be left open but unset, and bait should be broadcast liberally inside the trap and up to 20m or so from it. This should be repeated two days later, and again on the fifth day, when only the bait inside the trap is replenished and the trap is set.

Once the traps are set they must be visited at least once a day. Single-catch traps in woods with a high squirrel population are worth visiting twice a day. When trapping success falls, the pre-baiting routine can be followed in another area and the traps moved. In some areas, for example near beauty spots or picnic places, cage traps must be carefully camouflaged to avoid vandalism or disturbance.

Squirrels caught in cage traps can be humanely dispatched by

Both single and multi-catch cages are usually best when baited with whole maize.

driving them from the trap into a sack. Once in the sack, the animal can be moved into a corner and killed humanely by a sharp blow on the head.

Poison Hoppers

We are grateful to the Forestry Commission for the following information, which is reproduced by their permission.

The anti-coagulant rat poison, warfarin, can be used to reduce squirrel populations in and around vulnerable forestry crops at the time of year at which damage is expected, in the same ways as recommended for the most effective use of traps. The animals must feed on the poisoned bait for several days in succession before they succumb. If their feeding is interrupted for a few days they may recover. Trials suggest that it will be six to ten days before bait-take reaches a peak and the majority of squirrels are feeding on the poisoned bait.

Poisoned wheat should not be prepared on a do-it-yourself basis from commercially available rat killer preparations. Poor mixing could create greater risks for other wildlife and domestic stock, and it is difficult to distribute the poison evenly over the whole wheat grains to give the low concentration required. If the poison is not evenly dispersed in the bait, a proportion of the squirrels feeding may not receive an adequate dose.

A mixture of poison, sticker and dye is available from Rodent Control Ltd, 70 Queens Road, Reading, Berkshire. This must be added to the bait as directed to give the correct concentration of warfarin on a given quantity of wheat.

Provisions of 1973 Grey Squirrels (Warfarin) Order

Poison	Warfarin: 3–(a-acetonylbenzyl)-4–hydroxycoumarin or its soluble salt.
Concentration	Not exceeding 0.02% weight warfarin/weight of bait.
Bait	Whole grains of wheat over which the warfarin is evenly distributed.
Method of Presentation: outside buildings	In a hopper made up of two components: i. a tunnel not less than 230mm long and not more than 100mm internal diameter or internal square dimensions, ii. a container of any size or shape to hold the poisoned bait. The container must be firmly attached to one end of the tunnel and securely closed when holding poisoned bait so that the bait is accessible only to animals which have entered and passed along the length of the tunnel. Access by an animal to the poisoned bait at the junction of tunnel and container must be at a gap not more than 20mm high and no wider than the tunnel.
inside buildings	As for rat control.
Excluded Counties (except inside buildings)	Northumberland, Cumberland, Westmorland, Durham, Lancashire, Norfolk, East Suffolk, Isle of Wight, Anglesey, Caernarvon, Denbigh, Flint, Merioneth, Cardigan, Montgomery, Carmarthen. (Areas are those defined before the 1974 reorganisation).

The use of warfarin for grey squirrel control in England and Wales is defined in the Grey Squirrels (Warfarin) Order 1973 made under the Agriculture (Miscellaneous Provisions) Act 1972. This specifies the bait, poison concentration, method of presentation and counties in which warfarin may be used. *Warfarin may not be used for squirrels in Scotland.* The limitations are designed to reduce the risks to other wildlife, particularly red squirrels, and to domestic stock.

Hopper Design

The most important feature of the legislation on the method of presentation is the definition of the hopper. Animals must only reach the poisoned bait by going through the tunnel. This considerably reduces the number of species of mammals and birds at risk

Poison hoppers for grey squirrels must conform to the provisions of the Grey Squirrels (Warfarin) Order 1973. Warfarin may now only be used between 15 March and 15 August.

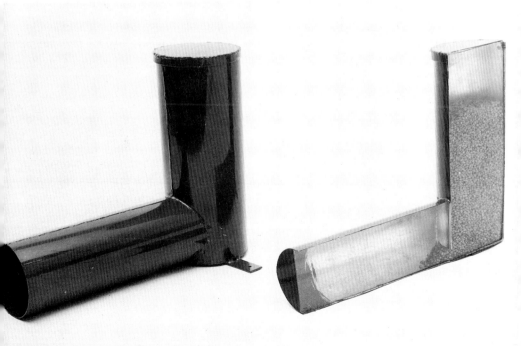

from feeding on the poison. The container may be of any size and shape, and from it the bait trickles into one end of the tunnel through a narrow gap. A large container (holding more than 5kg of bait) is probably inadvisable: if the poisoned wheat gets damp it may stick or begin to germinate and the bait may become less accessible and less palatable. While adequate hoppers can be produced by do-it-yourselfers, suitable hoppers holding about 2.5kg are available from Quadtag, Corry's, Roestock Lane, Colney Heath, Herts, AL4 0QW; tel: 0727 822614 or Oakwood Equipment Supplies, Oakwood Game Farm, Chichester, Sussex, PO18 9AL; tel: 0234 786701.

Hopper Siting

Hopper sites should be chosen in the same way and at the same spacing as single-catch cage-trap sites. The object is to get as many animals as possible feeding as soon as possible on the poisoned bait. It appears that approximately one hopper to four hectares of woodland is an average density but in some areas it will be necessary to increase or decrease this figure. It is unlikely that hoppers will need to be closer than one to one hectare. It should be remembered that it is important to reduce squirrel populations in woodlands adjoining vulnerable crops, as well as in the crops themselves, just before the damage season. Since poisoning involves perhaps one weekly visit (rather than five with pre-baiting and trapping) it is economical in labour.

When hoppers are first put out, a few handfuls of unpoisoned bait should be scattered around the site to attract squirrels. Yellow whole maize is attractive and shows up better than wheat and there is no risk that poisoned wheat is scattered by accident. The hoppers must be pegged or wedged firmly in position with logs and stones to guard against accidental spillage and camouflaged with branches and leaves to reduce the risk of interference. In some cases it may be advisable to sink the tunnel in the ground to keep the hopper upright and make the problem of camouflage easier. When this is done the earth should slope gradually down into the tunnel entrance

78

and the tunnel floor itself should be flat to prevent water running in. It is important that the tunnel should not be tilted down sufficiently steeply to allow bait to run down and encourage small mammals to scrape it out to the entrance. It is advisable, especially if hoppers are to be used in woodlands to which the general public has access, to have them clearly labelled POISON even where they have been camouflaged.

One visit weekly to a hopper holding 2.5kg of poison bait should normally be adequate. It may be worth checking hoppers a little more frequently when squirrel populations are high, particularly between the sixth and fifteenth days of poisoning. At each visit, the bait should be checked to make sure that moisture is not causing the grains to stick together in the gap and stop bait flowing freely from the container to the funnel. If a thin stick is used to free a blockage care should be taken to avoid pulling too much grain forward into the tunnel. Any spoilt bait should be removed from

Poison hoppers are best hidden to avoid the risk of damage by vandals.

the hopper and taken away for safe disposal. A scoop or jug is advisable for topping up the hopper with poisoned bait. It is important that any spillage at the hopper is cleared up at each visit and not allowed to accumulate. If badgers (or other animals) are tipping hoppers it may be advisable to lift the hoppers up on tables if is is not practicable to change the sites.

When poison ceases to disappear, the hopper may be left *in situ*, but must always be emptied. Unused bait may be spread under cover to dry and then stored in labelled polythene bags in a dry place.

Risks to Other Animals and Humans

The only risks to humans, domestic stock and game lie in misuse of warfarin. The risk to most other wildlife is reduced by the adoption of the tunnel entrance, but a few birds, small rodents and rats may explore such tunnels. Birds are extremely resistant to warfarin poison and no evidence could be found in field trials of deaths resulting from feeding on the poisoned grain. Small rodents (particularly wood-mice and bank-voles) in the vicinity of hoppers will succumb to the poison bait, but at the density required for squirrel control and at the time of year when poison can be effectively used, breeding in the unaffected population between hopper sites should provide adequate replacement. In the course of field trials it has not been possible to demonstrate any material effects on the overall population of small mammals in a woodland nor on the predators such as foxes, weasels, stoats or tawny owls to which voles and mice are important food items. To keep this risk as low as possible it is important that the numbers of hoppers used are kept to a minimum and that unused poisoned grain is removed from hoppers which are not in use.

The main areas in England and Wales with red squirrels (as shown in the Ministry of Agriculture Squirrel Survey 1972) have been protected by the legislation which precludes woodland owners and managers in those counties from poisoning grey squirrels. These areas of exclusion will be subject to regular review. In woodlands outside the excluded counties in which both red and grey squirrels are present, it is recommended that warfarin should not be used.

All users of warfarin in areas close to nature reserves should notify the appropriate County Naturalists Trust or Government body (English Nature, Scottish Natural Heritage, Countryside Council for Wales) of their intention to use poison.

Shooting with a Rifle

Squirrels can be stalked and shot with a .22 rifle and numbers may also be accounted for by the keeper as he makes his rounds. Stalking demands woodcraft, and speed and accuracy in shooting. As such it is a very much under-rated sport. The use of hollow point ammunition is advisable, and a telescopic sight will ensure accurate aiming and a clear sight of the target. By walking very quietly through a wood, or sitting down at a convenient spot, the rifleman will be able to hear and see squirrels in the branches, particularly in the very early morning. When feeding in the tree-tops on fir cones, acorns, chestnuts, beech mast and so on, squirrels are inclined to give their presence away by noise and by dropping debris on to the ground. On a still day in summer squirrels can be detected 100 yards away by the noise they make jumping from branch to branch. A chattering squirrel may well be interested in something other than the shooter and is often easy to stalk. Always remember your background when using a rifle.

Shooting in Woods with Shotguns

A good way to shoot squirrels in woods is for two Guns to work together, with a dog for marking. Dogs are attracted by squirrel scent and soon learn to mark a squirrel in the trees or spot it on the ground. When a squirrel freezes it can be difficult for one man to shoot it, as it moves its position with the shooter so as to keep behind the bough or the trunk. When two Guns are present, one should stand still and the other circle round the tree. The squirrel will usually watch the one who is moving, creep round the bough to avoid him and can then be shot by the stationary Gun.

Drey-poking

One way of reducing squirrels in a large wood is to quarter it systematically and poke out every accessible drey with sectional poles. This should be done in February and again in March. A wet and windy day or a very cold one will confine most squirrels to their dreys and ensure the best results. At least two Guns should be available to shoot the evicted squirrels. A useful squirrel-hunting team consists of three or more people, one with the drey-poking pole, one or two with shotguns for moving squirrels, and perhaps a rifleman for the occasional high static shot. Bags of seventy or more a day have been made by a drey-poking team.

Sectional rods of light alloy, specially designed for drey-poking and giving a maximum extension of about 12m, can be ordered from Quadtag Ltd. (tel: 0727 822614). Although the poles are light enough to be worked by one man, at full extension they are inclined to be whippy and are more easily controlled by two. It is important to touch the drey gently at the outset. Squirrels then come out cautiously, often singly, whereas a savage jab sends them springing rapidly away *en masse*.

New dreys can be recognised by the state of the leaf which the twigs bear, but even old dreys with withered leaves may hold a large number of occupants, particularly in the winter. It is essential to poke the dreys out thoroughly so that any young squirrels will fall to the ground where they can be despatched. If the dreys are completely destroyed rather than just damaged, only new dreys will be in evidence the following season and the drey-poking operations will be much quicker. This also aids the keeper later in the spring. Any new constructions in the woods are likely to be fresh corvid nests. Care should be taken not to damage the nests of birds of prey or other protected species. Old magpie nests should be dealt with at the same time, as they are often converted into squirrel dreys. One drey, preferably fairly accessible, can be left as a 'decoy drey' and may yield many squirrels throughout the year. A few light prods with a stick left permanently by the tree will bring out the squirrels to be shot.

Warning. Be careful when using metal drey-poking poles near high voltage cables! Also, take care that each section is properly locked in when putting them together. Sets of poles have been known to cause serious injuries if they come apart in use.

CHAPTER TEN

Conclusion

Long lines of decomposing animals on the gibbet used to be regarded as suitable evidence of a hard working and successful gamekeeper, and for some the old habit dies hard. Nowadays there cannot be a more provocative sight to any casual passer-by, or a worse advertisement of the keeper's trade. Predator control is an important and legitimate part of game management, but not by any means the only one. Any pests which cannot be recycled by feeding to the ferrets should be disposed of unobtrusively.

At one time a gamekeeper was often inclined to shoot first and ask questions afterwards, even if the quarry was only on his suspected list. It was perhaps an understandable point of view. Now, the law protects many – but not all – of the keeper's previous enemies, so additional effort must be concentrated on general game management, as well as the basic protection against the predators listed in this book.

It is acknowledged that the bulldozer is a far greater enemy to game in the long term than most predators. Habitat improvement may be the first priority; winter feeding may also be vital, or perhaps a change of policy on the agricultural chemicals in use. One aspect of game conservation complements another. Game Conservancy Ltd's Advisory Service will always help a shoot manager make the right decisions for the future. *A balanced approach to all the problems of wildlife conservation in a busy countryside has never been more vital than it is today.*

GAME CONSERVANCY COURSES

Residential Courses at Fordingbridge

Game Conservation and Shoot Management, annual in March

Gamekeepers' Refresher Course, bi-annual in March

Grouse and Hill Keepers' Course, bi-annual in April

Young Shots Course, annual in July or August

Part-Time Gamekeepers' Course, annual in September

Non-Residential Courses

Visitors' Game Management Days: a number of one-day Game Management Courses and Part-Time Gamekeepers' Courses are held throughout the country during the year.

For further details please contact the Advisory Department, Game Conservancy Ltd, Fordingbridge, Hampshire, SP6 1EF. Telephone: 0425 652381.

THE MINISTRY APPROVED TRAP

Higher specification. Complies with spring traps approval (variation) order 1988.

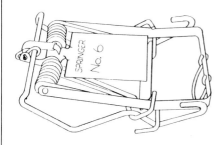 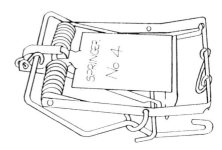

SPRINGER MULTI-PURPOSE NO. 6 RABBIT TRAP 6″ WIDE HEAVY DUTY. For setting in holes or tunnels. To kill Rabbits and Mink. Trap is complete with galvanized anchor chain and fitted with brass catch.

SPRINGER MULTI-PURPOSE NO. 4 RAT TRAPS 5″ WIDE. For setting in holes or tunnels. To kill Rats, Grey Squirrels, Stoats, etc. Trap is complete with galvanized anchor chain and fitted with brass catch.

Manufacturers of Springer Products No. 4 and No. 6. Including Scissor Mole traps. Fox Wires with swivel tying wire and loose safety stops. manufacturers of Self-locking Fox wires for use under licence. Cages for Rats. Squirrels, Mink, Fox, Rabbit and Feral cats.

GAMEKEEPA FEEDS LTD

INCUBATOR KITS (excl. Cabinet)
25, 50, 75 or 100 egg size

70 egg Incubators

BRINSEA INCUBATOR RANGE

ELECTRIC CONVERSION FOR GLEVUM

New and used Western, Bristol and other makes of Incubators
and Hatcher usually available

Spares for most Incubators.

Pheasant and Partridge egg size

INCUBATOR EGG INSERTS

Rotomaid Egg Washers and all spares

GAMESAN EGG WASH POWDER

QUALITY BREEDERS PELLETS

MAIL ORDER CATALOGUE AVAILABLE

THE GAME
CONSERVANCY

**SOUTHERLY PARK, BINTON
STRATFORD-UPON-AVON,
WARKS. CV37 9TU
BIDFORD (0789) 772429**
FAX (0789) 490536

TRADE MEMBER